When I Grow Up

Written by Jo S. Kittinger
Illustrated by Margeaux Lucas

SCHOLASTIC INC.

New York Toronto London Auckland Sydney
Mexico City New Delhi Hong Kong Buenos Aires

For the Leaky Pens, who helped me become an author
—J.S.K.

To my little nieces, Lauren and Ula
—M.L.

Reading Consultants

Linda Cornwell
Literacy Specialist

Katharine A. Kane
Education Consultant
(Retired, San Diego County Office of Education and San Diego State University)

ISBN 0-516-24815-4

12 11 10 9 8 7 6 5 4 3 2   7 8 9/0

Printed in the United States of America.   08

First Scholastic book club printing, November 2004

When I grow up,
I can be anything
I want to be.

A doctor.

A farmer.

An artist.

A truck driver.

A singer.

A teacher.

A clown.

A firefighter.

I could even be president.

**But today,
I just want to play.**

Word List (27 words)

a	doctor	president
an	driver	singer
anything	even	teacher
artist	farmer	to
be	firefighter	today
but	grow	truck
can	I	up
clown	just	want
could	play	when

About the Author

Jo S. Kittinger, a native of Florida, dreamed of becoming an astronaut when she was a little girl. Her strong imagination led to a world of adventures through words. In addition to writing, Jo enjoys nature, pottery, photography, and reading. While teaching her own children to read, Jo realized the critical role of emergent readers. She now lives in Alabama with her husband, two children, and three cats.

About the Illustrator

Margeaux Lucas was born in Ohio, but now resides in New York. She has been drawing constantly since she was four years old, so she always pictured herself an artist. Of course, there were times, while growing up, she thought of other careers like pastry chef or movie star. You will see a lot of her wishes in her illustrations.